This book belongs to:

hide
& Seek
in
hawai'i
3

A picture game for keiki

Find da kine!

Library of Congress Catalog Card
Number: 2003109633

First Printing, October 2003
1 2 3 4 5 6 7 8 9

Design by Jane Hopkins

ISBN 1-56647-643-7

Mutual Publishing
1215 Center Street, Suite 210
Honolulu, Hawai'i 96816
Ph: (808) 732-1709
Fax: (808) 734-4094
e-mail: mutual@mutualpublishing.com
www.mutualpublishing.com

Printed in Korea

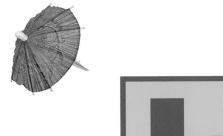

hide & Seek in hawai'i 3

A picture game for keiki

Text and Art Direction by

Jane Hopkins & Ian Gillespie

Photography by

Ray Wong

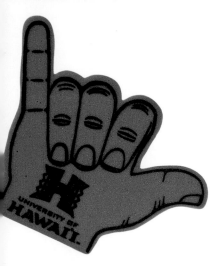

Mahalo Nui Loa to...

Malulani and David Bailey • Bailey's Antiques

Kara Gorgonio • Dole Plantation

Mr. and Mrs. Neil Halpin

Wayne Kieselbach • Kieselbach Woodworks

Glen F. Tomlinson • Koa Surf Classics & The Tomlinson Corporation

James Lenhart and Kevin Chang • Lion Coffee

Principal Silberstein, Mrs. Oliveira and Mr. Akamine • Palolo Elementary

Angie Britten • Lynn Cook • Colin Gillespie • Bennett Hymer
Jess Kroll • Mardee Melton • Alfred Monico • Patricia & Sam Polson • Nicole Sakai
Janet, Duke, Baron & Brittany Tomlinson • Gay Wong • Sistenda Yim

It's a picture game
of Hide and **See**k!

Hawai'i is full of fun things to seek,
lots hide inside, just take a peek…

Hawaiʻi is a place full of surprises,
where lots of things hide in many disguises.

Look in your school room and outside in the sun
and learn about Hawaiʻi—it can be fun!

Throughout these pages, I dare you to find
all the things listed within the rhymes.

And when you are done, there's so much more—
learn the Hawaiian word for train and boar.
Then go through the pages for a second peek,
you might find a dragon or a bird's beak.

Table of Contents

All Aboard the Sugar Train

In plantation days when sugar was at its peak,
the Waialua Sugar Train rolled by for you to seek...

A Christmas wreath and spool of thread,
a key, top hat and ball that's red.

Two Chinese coins and a little white dog,
a pencil, some scissors and a green frog.

A black chess queen and a dime not too far,
two jacks, a baseball and a yellow star.

Clean Your Room!
In your bedroom closet go ahead and peek
at all the stuff for you to seek...

Two baseballs, a flashlight and a yellow paddle,
the letter t, a blackjack and a shiny medal.

A marble and a bowling pin,
and a candy clown with a sideways grin.

A blue crayon, a yo-yo and the number 2,
a trophy, a dart and a red kazoo.

Gong Xi Fa Cai

**From the dancing dragon and all the food to eat,
Chinese New Year is the best time to seek...**

The letters that spell NEW YEAR and the number 3,
and three golden pigs that contain lucky candy.

One shiny white pearl, a red rubber ball,
and a 2 dollar bill—but that's not all.

A jade bracelet, matches, a spoon and then,
chopsticks, an umbrella and the number 10.

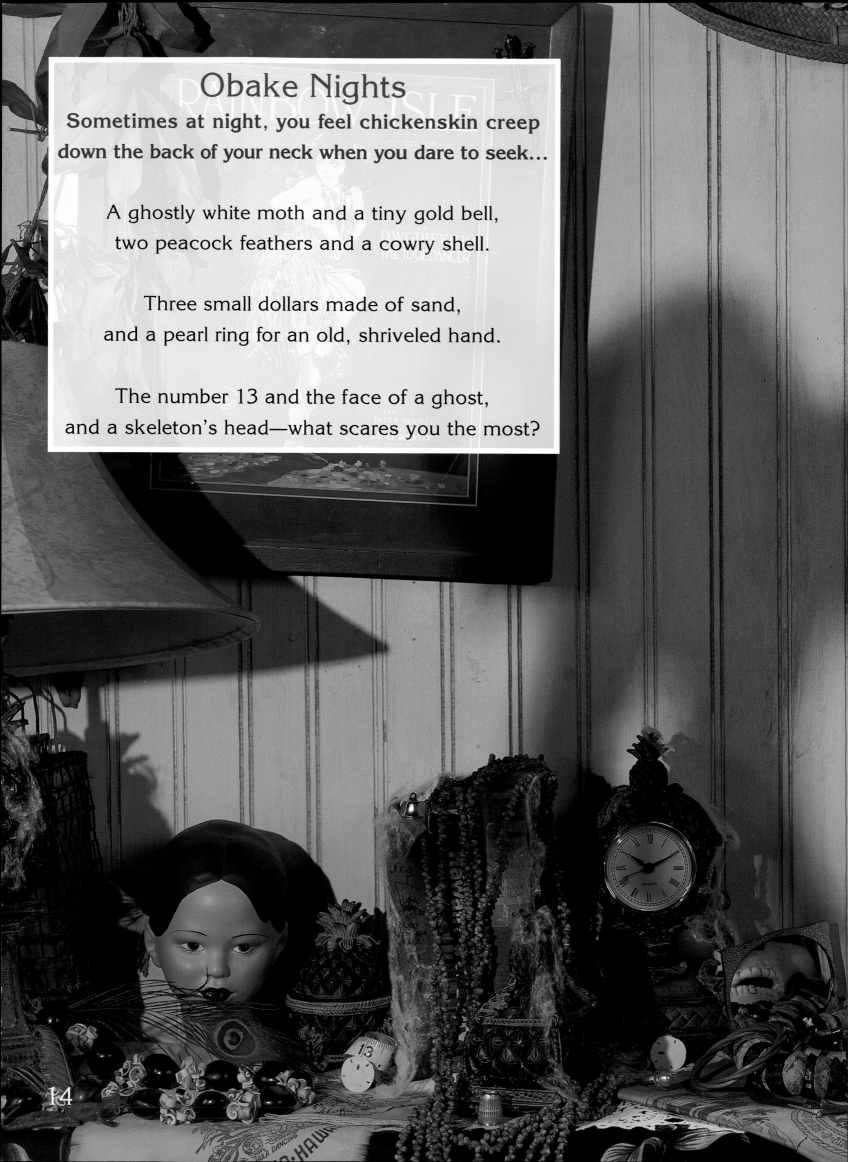

Obake Nights

Sometimes at night, you feel chickenskin creep
down the back of your neck when you dare to seek...

A ghostly white moth and a tiny gold bell,
two peacock feathers and a cowry shell.

Three small dollars made of sand,
and a pearl ring for an old, shriveled hand.

The number 13 and the face of a ghost,
and a skeleton's head—what scares you the most?

Hala Kahiki

Pineapples are juicy and so fun to eat,
still a symbol of Hawaiʻi, let's try and seek…

The letters that spell JUICE and a block letter R,
funky sunglasses and three tiny gold stars.

A pineapple knife and a turtle (or honu),
a Hawaiian flag, a button and the number 2.

A small, green umbrella to decorate a drink,
the words "Pali" and "Plantation" are somewhere, I think.

School Carnival

Going to the carnival is a very special treat,
after all that hard work, it's time to seek...

One yellow car and a seal doing tricks,
a big lollipop and three pixie sticks.

A ticket torn in half and three red darts,
two cell phones and a teeny, tiny heart.

The letters that spell FUN and a toy kazoo,
a monkey in a tree and only one duck that's blue.

Tailgating

Let's go tailgating at the end of the week,
before the game, there's always lots to seek...

Two ICEE® cups and one matchstick,
the letters that spell GO TEAM and four chopsticks.

A fork, a golf club and a radio,
57, a shaka and three geckos.

A bottle of shoyu and binoculars to see,
the number 5 and two fortune cookies.

Class Act

In your classroom during the long school week,
your teacher can show you lots of things to seek…

An egg timer, a robot and a sea shell,
a pink happy face and a shiny hand bell.

An apple for the teacher, an arrow and some glue,
a yellow crayon, a pig and a gecko, too.

And if your eyes are good, an orange bear is there,
But look very closely, I know it's somewhere.

Full of Beans

The coffee grown in Hawai'i cannot be beat,
it has a rich history and so much to seek…

A Kamehameha statue and a red number 10,
four coffee bag clips, a rainbow and then,

five coffee cups and the word SUN,
a butterfly, a tug boat—now isn't this fun?

A donkey, two coffee pots and 808,
a Hawaiian flag and Y because coffee is great.

Mele Kalikimaka

The night before Christmas, it's hard not to peek,
after Santa's arrived there's so much to seek...

A red ball ornament and two candy canes,
slippers, an apple and an airplane.

Two gingerbread men and a kukui nut lei,
a picture of a baby and Santa's red sleigh.

"To Malia from Santa" and a sea shell,
a pink umbrella and three Christmas bells.

Now look again throughout this book,
go on and try, just take a look.

Learn the Hawaiian word for things,
turn to a page, see what it brings.

When you look again, you just might find
something new you left behind.

Share your aloha every day of the week,
keep your eyes open and play hide and seek!

All these things hide for you to seek...

English	Hawaiian	English	Hawaiian
airplane	mokulele	box	pahu
apple	'āpala	bracelet	kūpe'e
arrow	kaha kuhi	broom	pūlumi
bag	'eke	butterfly	pulelehua
ball	pōpō	button	pihi
balloon	pāluna	calendar	'alemanaka
baseball	kinipōpō	camera	pahupa'iki'i
baseball bat	lā'au kinipōpō	can	kini
basket	'ie	candy	kanakē
basketball	kinipōpō hīna'i	car	ka'a
bell	pele	card (playing)	pepa hahau
bench	noho lō'ihi	cat	pōpoki
bird	manu	chair	noho
boar (pig)	pua'a	chicken	moa
book	puke	Chinese New Year	Konohī
boot	puki	chopsticks	lā'au 'ai
bottle	'ōmole	Christmas	Kalikimaka
bowl	'umeke	clock	uaki

English	Hawaiian	English	Hawaiian
clown	mea	flower	pua
	ho'omāke'aka	food	'ai
cobweb	pūnāwelewele	football	kinipōpō peku
coffee	kope	fork	'ō
coffee grinder	wili kope	frame	lā'au
coins	kālā pa'a	frog	poloka
conductor	alaka'i	gecko	mo'o 'alā
cookie	mea 'ono	ghost	lapu
cowry shell	leho	globe	pa'a poepoe
cup	ipu	goat	kao
curtain	pākū	hand	lima
dart	ihe	handkerchief	hainakā pa'eke
dictionary	puke wehewehe	hanger	kā
	'ōlelo	hat	pāpale
dime	kenikeni	helmet	mahiole
dog	'īlio	horse	lio lā'au
dollar	kālā	incense	mea 'ala
donkey	kēkake	jacket	iakeke
duck	kakā	jar	poho aniani
fan	pe'ahi	jewelry	lako kula
feather	hulu	key	kī
firecracker	pahūpahū	knife	pahi
fish	i'a	lamp	kukui
flag	hae	lion	liona

English	Hawaiian	English	Hawaiian
mango	manakō	pocket	pākeke
map	palapalaʻāina	present	makana
marble	kinikini	radio	lekiō
mask	makakiʻi	railroad	kaʻaahi
matches	pena ahipele	railroad track	alahao
medal	mekala	rainbow	ānuenue
mirror	aniani	ribbon	lipine
monkey	keko	rice	laiki
necklace	lei	ring	komo
needle (lei)	mākila	ruler	lula
newspaper	nūpepa	salt shaker	poho lūlū
notebook	kālana		paʻakai
number	hua helu	school	kula
orange	ʻalani	school house	hale kula
ornament	wehi	scissors	ʻūpā
palm tree	pāma	scoop	kīʻoʻe
paper cup	ipu pepa	seal	ʻīlio-holo-i-ka
peacock	pīkake		uaua
pearl	momi	shark	manō
pen	peni	shell	pūpū
pencil	penikala	shirt (aloha)	palaka aloha
photograph	kiʻi	shoe	kāmaʻa
pineapple	hala kahiki	sign	hōʻailona
platter (wooden)	papa lāʻau	skates	kāmaʻa holo paheʻe

English	Hawaiian	English	Hawaiian
skull	iwi poʻo	thimble	komo
sleigh	waʻa holo hau	ticket	kikiki
slipper	kāmaʻa pale	today	kēia lā
	wāwae	tomorrow	ʻapōpō
snake	naheka	tongs	ʻūpā
socks	kākini	toothpick	lāʻau ʻōhikihiki niho
soda	koka	towel	kāwele
spool of thread	pōkaʻa lopi	toy	mea pāʻani
spoon	puna nui	train	kaʻaahi
star	hōkū	trolley	kaʻa uila
station (railway)	hale hoʻolulu	trophy	lanakila
statue	kiʻi	truck	kalaka
steamboat	mokuahi	turtle	honu
straw (drinking)	mea omo	umbrella	māmalu
sugar cane	kō	watch	uwaki
surfboard	papa heʻe nalu	wheelbarrow	huilapalala
surfer	heʻe nalu	window	pukaaniani
tape	leki	wreath	lei
teapot	ipu kī	yesterday	nehinei